Abigail Toenail
and the Clipper
of Doom!

INTRO TO PHASE 5

/oe/

Level 4+
Blue+

Helpful Hints for Reading at Home

The graphemes (written letters) and phonemes (units of sound) used throughout this series are aligned with Letters and Sounds. This offers a consistent approach to learning whether reading at home or in the classroom.

THIS BLUE+ BOOK BAND SERVES AS AN INTRODUCTION TO PHASE 5. EACH BOOK IN THIS BAND USES ALL PHONEMES LEARNED UP TO PHASE 4, WHILE INTRODUCING ONE PHASE 5 PHONEME. HERE IS A LIST OF PHONEMES FOR THIS PHASE, WITH THE NEW PHASE 5 PHONEME. AN EXAMPLE OF THE PRONUNCIATION CAN BE FOUND IN BRACKETS.

Phase 3			
j (jug)	v (van)	w (wet)	x (fox)
y (yellow)	z (zoo)	zz (buzz)	qu (quick)
ch (chip)	sh (shop)	th (thin/then)	ng (ring)
ai (rain)	ee (feet)	igh (night)	oa (boat)
oo (boot/look)	ar (farm)	or (for)	ur (hurt)
ow (cow)	oi (coin)	ear (dear)	air (fair)
ure (sure)	er (corner)		

New Phase 5 Phoneme	oe (toe, foe, aloe)

HERE ARE SOME WORDS WHICH YOUR CHILD MAY FIND TRICKY.

Phase 4 Tricky Words			
said	were	have	there
like	little	so	one
do	when	some	out
come	what		

TOP TIPS FOR HELPING YOUR CHILD TO READ:

- Allow children time to break down unfamiliar words into units of sound and then encourage children to string these sounds together to create the word.

- Encourage your child to point out any focus phonics when they are used.

- Read through the book more than once to grow confidence.

- Ask simple questions about the text to assess understanding.

- Encourage children to use illustrations as prompts.

INTRO TO PHASE 5

/oe/

This book introduces the phoneme /oe/ and is a Blue+ Level 4+ book band.

Abigail Toenail
and the Clipper
of Doom!

Written by
William Anthony

Illustrated by
Irene Renon

What are you afraid of? Do you have a big foe?

Do you have a fear of a big monster on its tiptoes?

Are you afraid of a balloon that looks like a frog?

Abigail Toenail had a fear. She had a fear of one little thing.

To you and me, it was just a toenail clipper.

But to Abigail Toenail, it was the Clipper of Doom!

Abigail Toenail had never let the clipper near her toes.

Abigail Toenail's toenails were not little or short.

They did not fit in her bed. They did not fit in her room.

"Abigail, can I cut the toenails?" said Dad.

But Abigail did not let him near her with the Clipper of Doom!

Plus, Abigail Toenail's toenails were good for some things.

There was a cat stuck in a tree with no help in sight.

But Abigail was there to help. Up on her tiptoenails and the cat was back down!

A man went to rob a bank. Not so quick!

Abigail was there to help. The man fell on Abigail's toenails!

But the longer the toenails got, the harder it was to keep them fresh.

A spritz of an aloe smell did not stop the stink.

A scrub with a big brush did not stop it at all.

The smell was so bad that Dad said,
"Lock it in and block it all off."

Abigail's toenails were too much for her, too. She got Dad to come in.

It was hard for Dad to see in the green mist.

Her toenails were so bad that Abigail said, "Get the Clipper of Doom."

Dad went to clip, but the nails were too thick!

The cops said they had a man. He was right for this job.

The man from the bank took his cutters and went snip, snip, snip!

Abigail Toenail and the Clipper of Doom!

1)   What is Abigail afraid of?

2)   How do Abigail's toenails help her do good things?

3)   What does the man from the bank clip Abigail's toenails with?

a) A hacksaw

b) Cutters

c) The clipper of doom

4)   Have you ever had to face one of your fears? How did it make you feel?

5)   What does it mean to be brave?

©2022 **BookLife Publishing Ltd.**
King's Lynn, Norfolk PE30 4LS

ISBN 978-1-80155-052-9

Abigail Toenail and the Clipper of Doom!
Written by William Anthony
Illustrated by Irene Renon

An Introduction to BookLife Readers...

Our Readers have been specifically created in line with the London Institute of Education's approach to book banding and are phonetically decodable and ordered to support each phase of the Letters and Sounds document.

Each book has been created to provide the best possible reading and learning experience. Our aim is to share our love of books with children, providing both emerging readers and prolific page-turners with beautiful books that are guaranteed to provoke interest and learning, regardless of ability.

BOOK BAND GRADED using the Institute of Education's approach to levelling.

PHONETICALLY DECODABLE supporting each phase of Letters and Sounds.

EXERCISES AND QUESTIONS to offer reinforcement and to ascertain comprehension.

BEAUTIFULLY ILLUSTRATED to inspire and provoke engagement, providing a variety of styles for the reader to enjoy whilst reading through the series.

AUTHOR INSIGHT:
WILLIAM ANTHONY

Despite his young age, William Anthony's involvement with children's education is quite extensive. He has written over 60 titles with BookLife Publishing so far, across a wide range of subjects. William graduated from Cardiff University with a 1st Class BA (Hons) in Journalism, Media and Culture, creating an app and a TV series, among other things, during his time there.

William Anthony has also produced work for the Prince's Trust, a charity created by HRH The Prince of Wales, that helps young people with their professional future. He has created animated videos for a children's education company that works closely with the charity.

INTRO TO PHASE 5
/oe/

This book introduces the phoneme /oe/ and is a Blue+ Level 4+ book band.